D0093041

WILD PLANTS IN FLOWER

Fraser's Magnolia

A white pattern of floral antiquity, *Magnolia Fraseri* displays its spiral symmetry in the dim light of a moist southern Appalachian cove. The genus is symbolic as an ancient member of the "mother-type" forest which nurtured the deciduous associations of eastern North America. Its flower-of-many-parts typifies the primitive angiosperms. Attracting beetles with odors distinctly promising food, the flower literally traps its visitors in a meal-become-maze of staminodia and tepals. The ensuing struggle dusts mature stigmas with pollen borne from a distant tree—the strategic genetic gift of "otherness."

From nature

by TORKEL KORLING

WILD PLANTS IN FLOWER
3

EASTERN DECIDUOUS FOREST

Essay and species notes

by ROBERT O. PETTY

Evanston, Illinois, 1977

Botanical Books and Prints
from nature by TORKEL KORLING

1958 Wild Flowers. Portfolio 16½ x 22 inches. 11 plates. Published and distributed by Container Corporation of America, Chicago. Out of print.

1960 Glory by the Wayside. Book 5 x 7½ inches. 21 plates. Published and distributed by R. R. Donnelley & Sons Company, Chicago. Out of print.

1963 Spring Wild Flowers. Classroom study prints 13 x 18 inches. 8 plates. Society for Visual Education, Chicago.

1963 Wild Plants in Flower: plates xlii to xlix. Portfolio 16 x 22 inches. 8 plates. Second printing, 1966, for Field Museum of Natural History, Chicago. 4 plates. Out of print.

WILD PLANTS IN FLOWER: habitat series, with Diane F. Korling, editor.

1972 The Prairie—Swell and Swale. Out of print.

1973 Boreal Forest and Borders. Out of print.

1974 Deciduous Forest. 1st Printing. Out of print.

1974 Deciduous Forest. 2nd Printing. Out of print.

1977 Eastern Deciduous Forest, revised edition of Deciduous Forest.

In preparation:

 Wetlands and Quiet Waters.

 Beaches, Dunes and Sandy Woods.

Revised Edition of Deciduous Forest.
Wild Plants in Flower: Eastern Deciduous Forest.

Book format and illustrations
Copyright © 1974 by Torkel Korling
Evanston, Illinois 60118

Essay and species notes
Copyright© 1974 by Robert O. Petty

ISBN: 0-930404-01-7

Printed in U.S.A.

Deciduous Forest

With this third in the series we come to the North American wildflowers probably most familiar in the actual experience of most people. Here are the spring-blooming species remembered from the picnic ground, schoolhouse grove, the woodlot—the forest preserve. Through the Northeast, across the Midwest, deciduous forest is where the people are—or where they spent their childhood.

But if nostalgia is what we mainly bring to this experience of spring wildflowers, there is more we can carry away. A longer look back, a deeper look, at the strategies of deciduousness and of species survival, are provided by Dr. Robert O. Petty, Associate Professor of Biology and curator of the herbarium at Wabash College in Indiana. A fellow of the Indiana Academy of Science, he chaired its Natural Areas Committee from 1966 to 1973, and has served as chairman of both its Taxonomy and Ecology Divisions. In addition to scientific papers, Dr. Petty has published poems, essays and feature articles in various books and journals. His essay on prairie appeared in the National Geographic Society's 1973 book *Wilderness USA*.

Dr. Petty's backyard Spring-beauties bloom under a monumental beech tree, ours at Dundee under oak and hickory. It is not within the scope of this little book to tell why; several among the suggestions for further reading provide definitive discussions of the distributional complexities touched on in his essay. It has been our intent, through the subjects included here, to suggest such variety, while focussing on the essential continuity of the historic forest. The sequence of the illustrations approximates the species' time of coming into bloom, exaggerating, if anything, their brief spring season in the still open woods.

TORKEL KORLING

COVER. Spring light in a young forest, a crowd of
Trillium above decaying leaves—we have been here
before. But long before us, before the millenia of
glaciers brought summer as but a taunting of the
sun, recurrent drought had shaped evolving strategies—autumn and spring of the deciduous forest,
where to survive was to win by loss, or not at all.
Slowly our curve of earth tilts south again, and here
and there we find the ancient secret.

Prologue

There will always be a difference between enjoying a cultivated
garden bloom and what we feel upon discovering a native wild
flower. It is not just serendipity—the unpromised, undiminished
beauty. Somehow, we perceive the greater transience of a natural
thing which tempers our joy with something more profound.
True art makes image of those moments. These remarkable
photographs by Torkel Korling share such moments from
a lifetime of discovery.

    More than forty-two hundred plant species have been described
as residing within the area of the eastern deciduous forest.
This group of forty-four, here fixed in time, is but a sampling of
a world too rarely seen, that secretly comes and goes,
caught up in the ancient purpose of the sun, among the tall shadows,
about our busy lives, in "the woods of home."

Origins

It was the deciduous forest which nurtured and shaped technological man. No other vegetation on earth has absorbed so utterly the impact of "the tool-maker" as the temperate summer-green forest of the Northern Hemisphere. We still live amid its remnants. How did that forest come to be?

For the most part, the forests we know are "woods." A woods is our name for a particular stand of trees, found today most frequently as a biotic island in a sea of domestic monoculture—a small fragment left from a once vast green expanse, rich, varied and ecologically resilient.

Given a score of years, cleared forest land is gradually transformed through a succession of early weed, forb and grass to blackberry briars and goldenrod and, following that, a brush fallow of young saplings. Another ten years, twenty, a half-century, and once again a vigorous forest prevails, layered with small trees, shrubs and flowering herbs. Most of the woods we know have developed in this way, as adaptive secondary growth, following disturbance.

The particular combinations of forest trees we walk among have had an older origin. They have assembled variously across vast landscapes, advanced and retreated as climates shifted. Forests are still adjusting to the broad displacements caused by the recent glaciers. Finally, a forest has an origin which occurs over much longer geologic time, species by species, as adaptive forms evolve—a flower, a fruit—a way to move about and be. A forest then is a sum of origins.

It is difficult to imagine a world without flowers, yet we know that in the earth's chronology, flowers are a relatively recent innovation. Nearly two hundred million years ago the earth's domination by ferns and other spore-producing plants climaxed with the coal-age floras. Later, by the time the dinosaurs were thriving, gymnosperms and seed ferns flourished across the continents. Some seed plants such as the gymnosperms which today dominate the boreal forest (spruce, fir, and other conifers) produce naked seeds.

Botanically, a flowering plant, or angiosperm (producing enclosed seeds), is a plant which produces a fruit. A fruit develops from a flower and contains the seed. While the precise ancestor of the flowering plants is not yet clear in the fossil record (and may never be), most botanists agree that flowering plants probably evolved from an advanced type of seed fern over one hundred and twenty million years ago.

During this late Mesozoic Period, North America was uniformly warm and wet. A dense forest extended from Iceland to Alaska. Gradually, sea levels began to change. Continents were drifting. Soon the earth was in upheaval, a revolution of mountain-making—the Himalayas, the Alps, the Andes, the Rockies. Older mountains such as the Appalachians were once again uplifted. The physiography of earth was becoming intricately diverse. It was during this time that gymnosperm floras began to wane in the shadow of the rapidly-evolving flowering plants.

To fill the newly-fashioned environmental niches, new kinds of survival strategies were required. The ancestral woody plants perfected deciduous habits, devised shorter life cycles, while many were reduced to ephemeral herbaceous growth.

During the last sixty million years, three major environmental forces substantially affected the vegetation of North America. One of these was continued uplift of the Rocky Mountains, which produced a vast eastward rainshadow driving the mixed deciduous forest before it. A second force was the onset of lowering temperatures over the whole northern hemisphere, which together with altered precipitation patterns culminated in glacial climates. A third factor was the rejuvenation of erosion in the eastern landscapes by renewed uplift of the Appalachian mountains. As a result of all of these forces the mixed forest was segregated by a physiographic and climatic pattern.

Following the most recent glaciation of some twenty thousand years ago, deciduous trees left their glacial refugia, invading the wake of the retreating boreal forest. Slowly along the sheltered river courses where erosion inched its way into the boulder-strewn uplands, the mixed forest began to move. Wherever a fruit or seed could be carried, by wind or water, mammal or bird, seedling by seedling, the forest returned.

Harbinger-of-spring
Erigenia bulbosa / APIACEAE

Harbinger-of-spring, known to many as Salt-and-pepper, tests the reality of a late March morning. Protecting emerging plants from dessication, wintered Beech leaves insulate a soil teeming with life awakening to the promise of a warm and longer light. The species epithet, *bulbosa*, suggests one evolutionary stratagem common in a deciduous forest niche. The energy-rich perennial bulb can initiate early flowering and new leaves, allowing the plant to complete its life cycle before the new tree canopy shuts out the sun.

In the southeast, out of the Great Smoky Mountains, the forest crossed the Cumberland Plateau, spread along the flood plains of the Clinch River Valley, down the canyons of the Green and the Tennessee. In the north from along the Alleghenies, the new forest turned west, across glacial minted soils, then moved down the vast meltwater drainage of the Ohio.

New forests, new genetic potential, new ecological affinities were once again segregating: forests of chestnut and oak; forests of oak, hickory and yellow poplar; forests of beech and maple; of maple and basswood; and in the north, these and other hardwoods mixed with hemlock and pine. A rich mosaic of coves, dry hillsides, bogs and wetlands, soils lime or acid—adapted to each was a complex of forest species.

Sharp-lobed Hepatica
Hepatica acutiloba / RANUNCULACEAE

Common to rich mesic woods, Hepatica is one of the first spring flowers; it may be seen blooming out of melting snow banks on south-facing slopes, where its thick, fibrous roots allow it to occupy rather dry summer sites. This species favors less acid soils than its relative *H. americana*, whose blunt leaves are seen with Dwarf Ginseng (page 65). The three-lobed, liver-shaped leaves persist through winter and may remain green under snow cover or on more protected sites. Its name is a classic example of the herbalists' "doctrine of signatures." A tannin extract of the leaves was administered to those of torpid liver or having black (*melan*) bile (*cholo*). While such brew probably did as much to induce melancholy as to cure it, the plant was used medicinally in both this country and Europe into the last century.

Sharp-lobed Hepatica

Three to four thousand years ago, climates became warmer and drier than they are today. Xeric oak forests were encroaching far to the east and north, crossing the St. Lawrence Valley into southern Quebec. During this time, which ecologists call the xerothermic period, northern conifers and hardwoods retreated to local refugia where steep-walled valleys, north-facing slopes, moisture seeps or cold air drainage preserved a vestige of their earlier climate.

Gradually a cooler time returned. Oak domination of the forest weakened. The Greek and Roman world had come and gone when climates became steadily warmer once again. In the 11th century, another xerothermic interval entrenched the oak forests into a distribution much like that of today. Again the climate cooled. In the 17th and 18th centuries, a "little ice age" brought the coldest winters since the major glacial retreat, ten thousand years before.

Blue Cohosh
Caulophyllum thalictroides / BERBERIDACEAE

Arising amid the previous year's stalks, blue-green to purplish shoots raise their large triple compound leaves and developing flower clusters on a cold April morning. A broad-ranging species, also found in Japan, it is of special significance to biogeographers as a floristic member of a Tertiary vegetation once common to North America and Asia. It accomplishes cross-pollination by maturing the pistils of any given flower before the stamens. The flowers, pollinated by bees, mature into beautiful poisonous fleshy seeds. Its generic name refers to the "stem-like leaves" similar to those of Meadow Rue, *Thalictrum*. Other common names include Papoose-root, Squaw-root and Blue Ginseng.

Blue Cohosh

In the rich ground north and west of the Ohio, dry upland forests of oak and yellow poplar were relentlessly invaded by mesic species, beech and basswood, sugar maple and ash. Forests were re-aligning their strategies everywhere across the eastern landscape. Along the tension zones of merger between different forest types, replacement succession was underway. A windthrow, a seedling at a time, across a thousand miles, the ancient, root-anchored forests were slowly changing once again.

In the late 1700's, settlers reaching a crest of the Wilderness Road in a notch of the Cumberlands stood blinking into the western light across the greatest deciduous forest that ever was.

Twin-leaf
Jeffersonia diphylla / BERBERIDACEAE

The characteristic cleft-leaf which prompts this plant's common name is occasionally confused with the dissected leaf of Bloodroot, pictured next. The flower is also quite similar both in color and petal number. Though it flowers a month earlier than Mayapple (page 63), the two are related by family as close examination of leaf and flower structure will reveal. Twin-leaf is found on calcareous soils in rich woods. An original medicinal use is indicated by another common name, Rheumatism-root. The genus name commemorates our presidential patron of science.

Twin-leaf

Remnants

How do you make a cornfield out of a forest? How do you make a town? How do you clear away trees five feet through and towering one hundred and fifty feet? Forty acres, eighty, a section, a county— how do you "cut the top off" all the flat land between the Cumberlands and the Mississippi?

Our minds can only ache to comprehend.

Bloodroot
Sanguinaria canadensis / PAPAVERACEAE

This genus is indigenous to Atlantic North America and was well-known to the Indians whose name for it, Puccoon, reveals its use as dye. One of our most common spring flowering plants, it is frequent in rich April woods. Its perennial root stalk "bleeds" a bright red latex when cut. A member of the Poppy family, it contains a potent alkaloid which historically had wide medicinal use for both stimulant and presumed narcotic powers.

Bloodroot

Looking west from the Appalachians men spoke of an "ocean of trees" rolling on and on until it met a "sea of grass." There remains the image of a man cutting a tree in that green ocean—all around him is the damp hush when the wind dies into miles of towering shadows and green-filtered light. The ringing of his axe, his shout to no one, the creaking collapse and crash of the tree, the rustle of drifting leaves—all vanish into a sudden stillness that slowly yields to the late summer drone of insects. He squints at the immense circle of light as the silence rolls over him again. And again he is alone with the pounding of his heart and the noise of his own mind. He has marked the wilderness and he has heard its answer.

Spring-beauty
Claytonia virginica / PORTULACEAE

This is one of three species of Spring-beauty to be found across America. A small form, *C. caroliniana*, occurs in the eastern states, while *C. lanceolata* extends from the Rocky Mountains to the Pacific. Abundant, widespread and familiar, the early white to pink or pink-striped flowers are common throughout April and early May in the partial shade of lawns and parks as well as damp, deciduous woods. The plants arise from bulb-shaped tuberous roots. While the starchy perennial root is quite edible and was highly prized by Indian children, its small size, depth and the resulting sacrifice of the plant make questionable its use as food today.

Spring-beauty

Oak and hickory; beech, maple and elm; poplar and walnut—chip by chip, the stutter of axes echoed in the winter hills. Year after year, men felled the small trees and girdled the barks of the larger ones to kill them. Eighty trees to an acre was the average. First-year corn was planted under a lattice of dead branches, and remnant wild flowers crowded the stump-twisted rows. More winters, more trees girdled and some of the dead ones felled or burned where they stood; cold, seasoned wood was split into rails to fence the cattle out. With enough sons and neighbors a man might make a stumpland farm in a score of years, but battling the trees consumed three generations. Life was a long-handled axe and a crosscut saw.

Dutchman's-breeches
Dicentra Cucullaria / FUMARIACEAE

In forests with deep leaf mold, this species has its maximum development, and often forms dense carpets. Favored also are moist, shady ledges, north-facing slopes and river banks. The Greek genus name literally means two spurs. This characteristic shape suggests Dutch pantaloons hanging upsidedown. The flowering stalk and leaves develop from a small cluster of white to pinkish perennial corms. In settlement days, cattle grazing *Dicentra* foliage from woodlot pastures in early spring were occasionally poisoned by the plant's toxic alkaloids.

Dutchman's-breeches

"Sugar and Walnut Land" read the plat books of the original land surveyors: it meant the soil was calcium-rich. The pragmatic frontier farmer quickly learned that sugar maple and walnut meant rich loam, prized as potential cropland. Government Land Offices set these sections of ground as much as fifty cents to a dollar higher per acre—which might double the price.

We can only imagine the confusion, the boisterous promise of those early days. We can hear the thudding of axes, the songs, the shouts of log-rolling fellowship around incessant fires.

Squirrel-corn
Dicentra canadensis / FUMARIACEAE

Usually a week later in initial flowering and somewhat less common than Dutchman's-breeches, this plant also differs by having fragrant flowers and more deeply dissected leaves which are slightly whiter beneath. Its flowers, though white, have a distinctive shape reminiscent of the cultivated Bleeding Heart. The spherical, yellow-orange tubers resemble grains of corn and their being taken as food by squirrels accounts for the common name. It is seen here with typical ecological associates— Recurved Trillium, Solomon's-seal and Fragile Bladder Fern (*Cystopteris fragilis*).

Squirrel-corn

For the rich, clearing crews "made land" and sold back timbers. Cabin logs were a penny a foot, hewn square. In time, water-powered sawmills would rip the trees to lumber. Yellow poplar, white oak, white ash and hickory—a wood for every need—for buildings, tools and wagons; for furnishings, maple, cherry and walnut; burnished "curly maple" for the stocks of the frontier rifles; oak, walnut and locust for fence rails—a wood for every purpose from cradles to coffins. Never had civilization been so rich in wood. By necessity, wood was used for every fashioned article of living. Even so, most of the trees were rolled together and burned. The greatest resource need was land for crops.

Toothwort
Dentaria heterophylla / BRASSICACEAE

Toothwort is seen here under Oak canopy on an acidic mossy slope. The genus is so named because of the ivory colored tooth-shaped rhizome from which the flowering stem arises. The basal leaves of this species are different from those of the stem leaves—hence the species name, *hetero* (different), *phylla* (leaves). The similar and somewhat more north-ranging Cut-leaf Toothwort (*D. laciniata*) displays a lacy foliage differing principally in its absence of such basal leaves.

Toothwort

Like the first farmsteads, towns of the frontier were built in stumpland meadows. The trees were gone. The civic landscapes sweltered in the sun. Never so quick an afterthought: fast-growing black locust trees were imported and planted everywhere, from college campuses to courthouse squares, to provide a promise of shade. What irony—the sons of the world's most incredible axemen planting seedlings in the shadow of stumps five feet across.

Bluets

Houstonia caerulea / RUBIACEAE

Delicate stems and flowers of this member of the Madder family crowd above old litter and roots of Beech. This species of Bluets is but one of over two dozen in North America. Frequently found in soils of low fertility both in the open and in drier woods, it is also common to lawns, meadow and forest margins. The genus is named for the 18th century English botanist and physician, William Houston. This species has many common names, among which are Quaker Ladies and Innocence. The Beech root sprout seen budding here reveals a strategy which permits the eventual dominance of Beech over Maple in climax forest. With the decline and death of the main trunk, lateral sprouts nourished by old, residual roots can become new trees.

Bluets

At the edge of the small towns a Chautauqua grove had been left perhaps, or a fairground park, and here and there a pasture-woodlot. Trees were left at each end of plowed fields, where the horses could rest in shade at the end of a furrow. In wetlands, swamps and river bottoms, on steep hillsides and in the hollows, wherever corn would not grow—or later, beyond the easy reach of lumbermen and the footing of mules or oxen—the trees were left alone. But on the upland, most of the great forest was gone.

Later, traveling crop-seed salesmen would offer fast-growing evergreen seedlings as a promotional enticement. Still today the old flat top "homestead pines" can be seen scattered through the farmlands. Oak, chestnut, walnut, maple, elm—for the most part, what remained of the once-great forest were the names of a few city streets.

Yellow Trout-lily
Erythronium americanum / LILIACEAE

This beautiful member of the Lily family has many common names, including Yellow Adder's-tongue and the misnomer Dogtooth-violet (supposedly from the shape of the young white corm). John Burroughs coined the names Trout-lily and Fawn-lily, with reference to the spotted leaves, to avoid the confusion with Violet. Here the six reflexed tepals (units of the corolla lacking sepal-petal differentiation) are seen at pre-anthesis. The several species of *Erythronium* in North America include another yellow-flowered one of western mountains, and a tall pink-flowered species of Pacific states. The genus name derives from the red-flowered European species (Greek *erythros,* red).

Yellow Trout-lily

Tool-maker, destroyer of forests? We too are the children of the glacier, and all that we endured is etched into the cave behind our eyes. We moved against the wilderness with the careful, determined steps of survivors. The glaciers taught us to prepare for what was coming, made us perceive a future from the past each autumn in the fading light. How long ago we prayed the sun-god would return, and at a peak of sacrifice, some brief winter day, the sun did stop, come back. We burned our forest gods in celebration. In age-old festivals of season, our roots are deeper than we comprehend. And when we find the first wild flower in spring, we sense that primal knowing—somehow we too survived the glacial snows.

White Trout-lily
Erythronium albidum / LILIACEAE

This species of Trout-lily is somewhat less common in the northeastern forest than the yellow, becoming rare toward the East. It is readily distinguished by the color of the tepals and its less strongly mottled leaves. Like the Spring-beauty, these Trout-lilies may increase in woods opened by partial clearing or browsing of undergrowth. Both species propagate by offsets from a deep-seated bulb, and are frequently found blanketing an area. Germinated seedlings mature very slowly and a flower is not produced until the seventh year of growth.

White Trout-lily

Identities

The history of botany is a history of names: names of men who gave names to plants, which, in turn, often were the names of other men in commemoration. The flora of the New World was first being examined at a crucial time in the history of plant naming. The voyages of discovery were piling high the museums and herbaria of Europe with thousands of unknown species from around the world. Classifiers grappled with the problem of trying to make sense of the great diversity.

Recurved Trillium

Trillium recurvatum / LILIACEAE

Mottled leaves arrayed in mottled light, and the red-brown petals of recurved Trillium, seem the sum of April at a glance. The Trillium was wholly new to early colonists, for the genus does not occur in Europe. Its name comes from the Greek for three, referring to the number of leaves, sepals and petals. Also called Prairie Trillium, this species is conspicuous through the Oak forests that persist in the grassland border regions. The description "recurved" refers to the reflexed position of the sepals at anthesis, distinguishing it from the similar *T. sessile.*

Recurved Trillium

The man who would do most to rescue natural history from the deluge was born in 1707. He was Carl Linn of Sweden, whose published Latinized name, Linnaeus, became synonymous with plant knowledge and identification. Linnaeus was the dominant figure in European science for nearly a century, influencing three generations of botanists. With great energy and scholarship, he wrote extensively. His convenient rules of nomenclature allowed anyone to identify plants by merely counting the number of stamens and pistils. His exuberant teaching conveyed his enthusiasm to many talented students who combed the world for new plants. Several of his protégés visited the American colonies.

Wake-robin
Trillium erectum / LILIACEAE

Towering above Spring-beauty, one of the most familiar Trilliums, Wake-robin, stands open to the flies which pollinate it. Also called Stinking Benjamin, this species emits a strong malodorous message which guides the insects. Nearly all species of Trillium have been used medicinally in some manner. Wake-robin, especially, was sought by Indians and settlers. Preparations from its dried roots and rhizome were used for everything from a mild tonic to promoting parturition, the latter resulting in another common name, Birthwort.

Wake-robin

Europe had a great interest in the plants of America for potential medicinal and horticultural uses. Dispute over rights to the New World's forest resources, especially the great white pines for ship masts, was sufficient to become an article of war.

The great botanists of Europe, men such as Collinson and Fothergill in England, Gronovius in Holland, as well as Linnaeus, were receiving a lively traffic of seeds and plants from the colonies sent by interested laymen.

Two remarkably diligent and knowledgeable laymen who impressed these scholars were John Clayton, born in England but emigrated to the Virginia colony, and John Bartram, a self-educated farmer now regarded as America's first native-born naturalist. In 1728 Bartram began collecting and transplanting native species to his farm near Philadelphia as Clayton started a similar plantation near Williamsburg. With great vitality and native intelligence, both men built informal botanic gardens and corresponded with European scholars.

White Wake-robin
Trillium erectum forma albiflorum / LILIACEAE

Most species of Trillium are highly variable in form, size and color, even within a local population. This white form of the red Wake-robin, seen here among the leaves of False Solomon's-seal (page 61) and White Baneberry (page 75), is frequent in the species' eastern range. At least six forms have been formally designated and numerous others have been reported. Petals vary in pigmentation across white, yellow, green and red. Occasionally individuals occur with totally leaf-like petals—an interesting evolutionary clue. Trillium is also renowned for having the largest chromosomes thus far observed of all flowering plants.

White Wake-robin

John Bartram, especially, attracted many of the continent's prominent naturalists to his circle of friends. With Benjamin Franklin he established a group which would become the American Philosophical Society. Bartram acknowledged this cherished friendship in naming the rare genus *Franklinia*. The Bartram tradition was extended by his son, William, who became one of the first naturalists to explore the heart of the eastern deciduous forest in the southern Appalachian wilderness.

John Clayton's extensive notes and collections from Virginia were sent to Gronovius in Holland and, in turn, were studied by Linnaeus. In 1739, at the urging of Linnaeus, Gronovius (at his own expense) published Clayton's work as *Flora Virginica*, the first authoritative treatment of exclusively American plants. In honor of the man who had tramped the Virginia wilderness, Gronovius named one of the plants, Spring-beauty (page 19), for Clayton.

Gleason's Trillium
Trillium Gleasoni / LILIACEAE

A species of mesic old-growth forests, predominantly Mid-western, Gleason's Trillium carries the name of taxonomist and plant geographer Henry Gleason (see bibliography). It closely resembles Nodding Trillium (*T. cernuum*) in that both have declining peduncles; however, this plant has slightly larger flowers and longer peduncles, somewhat less reflexed. Minor differences further separate the two, including less petiolate leaves in *T. Gleasoni*. The plant is seen here shading a seedling of the canopy giant, Sugar Maple (*Acer saccharum*).

Gleason's Trillium

A century later at Deerfield School in New York, a young student, Asa Gray, pondered the identity of a familiar flower. As he recalled in later life, "I borrowed a copy of Eaton's manual, threw myself beneath the nearest tree and keyed my very first plant— *Claytonia virginica*." Gray had discovered a legacy as well, and indeed, so popularized the flora of eastern North America that he was hailed "father of American botany."

An old adage for botany students is, "If you don't know or can't remember the species epithet, call it *virginica, caroliniana* or *canadensis* and your chances are pretty good!" The degree of truth in this reflects, of course, the inordinate amount of original collecting and naming in the Virginia and the Carolina colonies and in neighboring Canada.

Virginia Bluebells
Mertensia virginica / BORAGINACEAE

During settlement when the forest was thinned and before the cattle were turned to graze, each spring waves of flowers flooded the opened woods. They spread as though released, as indeed they were, from tree roots and the heavy shade. Here old fashioned Bluebells, or Cowslips, pre-empt space and time in a young floodplain forest, where Hackberry saplings anchor the alluvium. This popular wildflower was frequently transplanted to homestead gardens in early days. Removing the plant from floodplain soils to those of the upland occasionally resulted in a shift of the flower color, from predominantly blue to reddish. The perplexing phenomenon is now explainable in terms of the anthocyanin pigment's response to soil acidity.

Virginia Bluebells

Early botanists like other natural scientists were predominantly physicians, for during the formative stages of science, higher education fell into relatively few distinct categories. History, for example, encompassed all recorded fact; philosophy concerned itself with the pursuit of new facts, new knowledge. A further dichotomy decisively separated man and nature—a condition which still prevails throughout much of higher education even in the "age of ecology." Hence, natural history and natural philosophy were the essentials of science.

Within this context, a young man of privilege studied toward one of the great professions—the clergy, law or medicine—or uninspired by these, he could turn to teaching or writing.

Great Trillium
Trillium grandiflorum / LILIACEAE

Here with a host of spring wildflowers, a colony of Great Trillium persists in a grazed woods. The impact of cattle is evidenced by the browsed root sprouts of Beech. Trout-lily and Violet, Spring-beauty and May-apple share this trampled ground—reminders of life's resilience in the midst of change.

Great Trillium

The only formal science training was in medicine and a large part of qualifying for a medical certificate involved the study of medicinal herbs, their recognition, qualities and useful preparation. Today we often use the term "botanize," as, to go botanizing. In an earlier age, the common term was "simpling." Medical herbs were "simples," that is, simple primary components of prepared compound medicines. Compounding the extracts as tinctures, emolients, infusions, decoctions, and so forth, was the medical art. Though qualified in medicine, as Linnaeus was, many scholars turned exclusively to the study of plants while continuing to lecture in medicine at the universities.

Common Blue Violet
Viola papilionacea / VIOLACEAE

So deeply rooted in the poetry of earth, this widespread familiar violet seems somehow to vouch for all violets in our memory—a vivid archetype in form and color. Small wonder there is often brief dismay in learning of the over 300 species of violets in the world, including the domestic Pansy, *V. tricolor*. Over fifty species occur in eastern North America. In addition, there are swarms of hybrids across each species range, and variations in form and color abound. The species seen here includes a form bearing whitish gray petals with blue veins which guide its pollinators. The more grayish form, *albiflora*, is called by many Confederate Violet.

Common Blue Violet

Strategies

What is a flower? To our mind's eye it is pattern and beauty. To
the evolving plant species it is much more, encompassing a whole
strategy of adaptation which is crucial to its survival. The flower has
been recognized as a sexual apparatus since the time of Rudolph
Camerarius in the late 17th century. Linnaeus further emphasized the
importance of plant sexuality and the role of floral parts. Seed
production and dispersal are two enormously important events in
the life cycle of a flowering plant, and a flower's form derives from
the functions that accomplish these. A fertilized flower matures into
a fruit and the fruit becomes the vehicle of dispersal. To be fertilized,
a flower must first be pollinated.

Sweet White Violet
Viola blanda / VIOLACEAE

The irregular flower of violets is a classic in pollination archi-
tecture. Again, in this white species, dark veins guide nectar-
seeking bees to a recessed corolla spur where secreted nectar is
collected. At anthesis, mature stamens partially obstruct the
bee's path, dusting the visitor with pollen for transport to a
neighboring or distant flower. In many violets, some of the
flowers remain unopened, and may even be borne underground.
This cleistogamy assures self-pollination—an example of
ecological strength, the exquisite balance between conservative
inbreeding of genetic fitness and liberal variation through
outbreeding. Have we looked at nature long enough to under-
stand?

Sweet White Violet

Flower structure at anthesis (the time of maximum exposure of flower parts) is primarily related to pollination mechanics. For example, an insect-pollinated flower may reflect the behavior of its pollinator. If a bee must land before approaching food, a flower must provide a place to land, and many flowers of irregular shape are doing just that, such as the violets. Many insects "feel insecure" in large open flowers like magnolia where there are no leading structures, and they do not land there but rather seem to seek fused flower-parts for tunneling. Beetles may come readily to the same flower which the bee avoided.

If a flower is pollinated by ground-walking flies such as fungus gnats, as is Wild-ginger (page 57), an obscure reddish-brown flower opening onto the ground is an effective habit.

Showy Orchis
Orchis spectabilis / ORCHIDACEAE

This species of rich slightly acid woods is seen here in a Hemlock refugium growing with the common Christmas Fern (*Polystichum acrostichoides*). While a major evolutionary trend in Orchids, and plants in general, has been toward fewer parts, through reduction and fusion, an exception in this group is a strategy dependent on an immense number of seeds. A single plant may produce over 200,000 seeds. Showy Orchis is, however, so strikingly beautiful as to imperil its own survival in any densely peopled region. The plants are taken from the wild and seldom prosper in cultivation due to their specific habitat requirements. Once rather common, the species survives today in declining numbers, primarily in remote areas or where it is afforded effective legal protection in parks and nature preserves.

Showy Orchis

Consider for a moment the evolutionary and ecological problems which any plant species must "solve." With an ultimate goal of survival, the species must accomplish a delicate compromise between its present adaptation and a preparedness for possible changes in the environment—the fitness-flexibility compromise. How is it accomplished?

The principal device lies in the reproductive or breeding system which the plant employs. A species may be essentially "outbreeding" wherein cross-pollination predominates, or it may be "inbreeding" or primarily self-pollinated. The benefit from each is clear. Self-pollination tends to preserve adaptive traits already possessed, but also risks combining deleterious genes. Cross-pollination generates new combinations of genetic traits, creating a variable population upon which natural selection can work.

White Clintonia
Clintonia umbellulata / LILIACEAE

This species is most prevalent in the Allegheny and Appalachian Mountains, found typically growing in cool, shaded ravines, especially on acidic soils underlain by sandstone. It is seen here growing with young Red Maple (*Acer rubrum*) under an Oak and Pine canopy. This is one of two species of *Clintonia* occurring in the eastern states. The more northern *C. borealis* has a smaller flower cluster which is yellow and which develops into vivid blue berries, while the larger white umbel of this species produces black berries. The genus is named for DeWitt Clinton, pioneer naturalist, a governor of New York.

White Clintonia

A frequently observed strategy which prevents self-pollination is simply a time separation between the maturation of male and female parts on the same plant. Throughout the families of such species as Toothwort, Goat's-beard, Twin-leaf and May-apple, the pistil and stigma mature before the stamens. Geranium is an example where the reverse is true. Diverse out-crossing strategies, however, reduce to one: to maintain a sufficient degree of variation from which adaptive genetic combinations may arise.

In some plant groups, unusual measures assure self-pollination, at least in part. In some cases the flower does not open. Many violets produce at least some of these cleistogamous flowers. Vegetative propagation of various types, such as rhizomes, root sprouting, or layering, can quickly perpetuate the current hereditary potential. Most plants have some combination of propagation strategies.

Crested Dwarf Iris

Iris cristata / IRIDACEAE

A diminutive plant rarely exceeding five inches in height, this woodland Iris is typical of the southern sector of the deciduous forest. In the northern reaches of its range, it may be encountered in protected sites, as here in lowland forest under Red Maple. The genus name is from the mythological goddess of the rainbow, an allusion to the diversity of flower color within the group. Here, too, is the inspiration for the royal emblem of the fleur-de-lis.

Crested Dwarf Iris

Without question, the greatest degree of co-evolution pertaining to flower structure relates to agents of pollination. Elaborate specializations abound. In addition, attractile chemistry often mimics other natural sensory stimulation which preconditions insect behavior. Included are such phenomena as female-scent signals to male insects.

Perhaps the most common types of attraction relate to the promise of food which the pollinating insect associates with the flower's odor, form or color. Food offering varies, from deceit or no food at all to the common solutions of sugars from nectaries. Food may be offered as expendable tissue, as in the sterile stamens of primitive magnolia or tulip tree flowers. Food as excess grains of pollen is a major inducement to certain insects.

Wild-oats
Uvularia sessilifolia / LILIACEAE

An evolutionary rift of over two hundred million years separates fern from flowering plant; Christmas Fern and Wild-oats here find a place together in a remnant forest. Rarely found in great numbers, this delicate sessile-leaved *Uvularia* is about half as large and much less frequently encountered than *U. grandiflora*. Both are commonly called Bellwort, sometimes Merrybells (not to be confused with the Bellflowers, genus *Campanula*). As are some fern shoots, the Bellworts are edible when cooked, their taste rivaling that of asparagus. Old culinary and medicinal usage gives us the term "wort," derived from Old English *wyrt*, meaning simply "plant".

Wild-oats

Attraction by deceit is common. For example, by their dead flesh odor mimicry, some Trilliums, Jack-in-the-pulpit and Wild-ginger attract various flies as effective pollinators.

Among the most complex pollination syndromes are those found in the Arum and Birthwort families to which Jack-in-the-pulpit and Wild-ginger belong. The flower structure of these plants constitutes an insect trap. The Wild-ginger has reflexed hairs which trap insects long enough to receive or deposit pollen.

Wild-ginger

Asarum canadense / ARISTOLOCHIACEAE

A low trailing plant, Wild-ginger arises from long-persisting, shallow, branching rhizomes. Its best growth is on moist, shady slopes and ravines. The bruised rhizome has a distinctive ginger-like odor although it is unrelated to true ginger, a tropical plant. The rhizome and root stalk were used by several Indian tribes as a condiment to mask the taste of bitter medicines. The Chippewa name for it meant "sturgeon plant," and ground, dried fragments were added to many strong fish to soften or improve the flavor. Pioneer women often cooked the dried rhizome with sugar, producing a palatable spice. The flowers, often inconspicuous beneath dense leaf cover, are visited by crawling insects.

Wild-ginger

The hooded spathe of Jack-in-the-pulpit is especially interesting. Flies attracted by the plant's carrion odor descend to the base of the spathe in search of food. Finding none, they attempt to fly out, but the entrance is obscured by the shadow of the hood. However, light is admitted through the "windows" in the walls of the spathe. The trapped insects fly repeatedly toward these sources of tissue-filtered light. In the species illustrated, reddish veins frame these windows and intensify the effect of the light signal. Flies buzz about, colliding with the male and female flowers. Whichever is mature, yields or receives pollen. Flies eventually escape by crawling up the inner spike or spadix over the basal flowers. At the top of the spadix, the exit is obvious to even a tired insect, which is then attracted, forgetfully, to a neighboring flower.

Jack-in-the-pulpit
Arisaema triphyllum / ARACEAE

This canopied "pulpit," spathe, and club-shaped spadix, or "Jack," mark one of the most widely known forest plants. There perhaps also should be a "Jill," as the species is occasionally dioecious, having only male or female flowers reaching maturity on an individual plant. Pollination is chiefly by flies which are attracted by a carrion odor. The plant arises from a deep bulbous corm, accounting for another common name, Indian Turnip. The alternatives Pepper Turnip, Dragon Root and Memory Root suggest a prank once played on novice woodsmen: biting into the corm (or any other part of the fresh plant) results in temporary but unforgettably intense burning and swelling of lips, tongue and throat. The active substance, which effectively protects the plant from grazing, is calcium oxalate, recognizable under microscopic view as innumerable needle-shaped crystals. Boiling makes the "turnip" quite palatable, by leaching out the oxalate crystals. Pictured here is probably the polyploid identified by some authors, for its reddishness, as *A. atrorubens* var. *triphyllum*.

Jack-in-the-pulpit

In geological time, flowering plant evolution closely parallels the evolutionary progress of the insects. While we normally think of the beneficial pollination role of insects, their threat to a flower is less often appreciated. The chief, highly adapted, nectar-feeding pollinators such as bees, wasps and butterflies had not evolved by the time angiosperms originated in the Mesozoic. Beetle fossils are abundant from this period, however. Beetle-pollinated plants, such as magnolia, are considered primitive. They have many expendable parts with which to feed their voracious pollinators. A widely respected theory which helps to explain the gradual evolution of the flowering plant, its ovary and fruit, suggests that a mechanical protection was needed against beetles or other primitive insects which readily ate the energy-rich tissues of developing seeds. Throughout their evolution, angiosperms have been devising effective protection. Their co-evolution with the insects, therefore, has involved both attractile and repellant tactics.

False Solomon's-seal
Smilacina racemosa / LILIACEAE

With obvious similarities to the true Solomon's-seal (page 83), this species differs markedly by presenting flowers in an intricate terminal raceme rather than at the leaf axis. It is a common sight in open, moist woods and valleys, ranging onto thinner soils and somewhat less mesic sites than Solomon's-seal. The inflorescence matures into a dense cluster of fragrant red berries flecked with purple. The fruit is edible raw or cooked. The scientific name means "little Smilax," there being a family relationship with that genus, but only a general similarity in form.

False Solomon's-seal

Many final pathways in a plant's chemistry lead to the synthesis of substances which make plants (especially their reproductive tissues) unpalatable to insects and larger herbivores. Many "waste" products such as metabolic acids are employed as a passive defense. High concentrations of organic acid alone can make plant tissue inedible. Nicotinic acid, derived from species of the Nightshade family, is an old, once widely-used insecticide, as are pyrethrums from the flowers of Chrysanthemum. Oxalic acid is neutralized to a calcium salt in many plants and stored as minute crystals in their cells. To eat such tissue is traumatic to an herbivore. Jack-in-the-pulpit (page 59) is a classic example of this strategy.

May-apple
Podophyllum peltatum / BERBERIDACEAE

Here is one of the most characteristic species of the deciduous forest, with a broad ecological latitude, extending from moist open woods and borders to clearings and wet meadows. Large colonies develop from long, creeping, perennial rhizomes. Two forms of the plant result from differing stages of maturation: single-leaved stems develop no flowers, while double-leaved, branched stems are fertile. Early settlers learned of the plant's "medicinal powers" from the Indians who used it for a wide variety of ailments. While leaves are toxic and avoided by grazing animals, the ripe fruit or "apple" (it is actually a berry) is edible and was used in jellies. The principal medicinal organ is the root, extracts from which have a purgative effect. The scientific name literally means shield-shaped (*peltatum*) foot-leaf (*podophyllum*). Other common names include Hog Apple, Raccoon Berry, Wild Lemon and Duck's Foot.

May-apple

Many protective plant chemicals are physiologically potent to insects, but often have a milder, though repellant effect on vertebrates by disturbing their metabolism. Such plants were discovered by man through trial and error and slowly became used as "drug plants" or as herbs and spices. Many herbs and spices were once medicines and, to obscure their pungent taste, they were sprinkled on food. This practice later became reversed, the medicine or spice "doctoring" the flavor of food.

A curiosity from one phase in the early history of plant naming is the doctrine of signatures, which found the efficacy of medicinal remedy denoted in the outward shape of the plant—a kind of hieroglyphic of God, a sign or signature of the plant's virtue. Plants with leaves shaped like a liver, such as Hepatica, were thus clearly meant as a curative for hepatic complaints. Our legacy from this quaint period is a wealth of common names from Lungwort and Liverwort to Adder's Tongue which cured the sting of the serpent.

Dwarf Ginseng

Panax trifolium / ARALIACEAE

Approximately one-half the size of its better known namesake *Panax quinquefolia*, this plant, also called Ground-nut, is seldom taller than eight inches. Its small whorl of three-parted leaves are given scale by the leaves of *Hepatica americana* and the curled leaf litter of Beech. "Ginseng" comes from the Chinese "jin chen," literally, man-like. This refers to the presumed similarity of the medicinal root stalk to the human form. Commerce in the dried roots of the larger species has so diminished it that one rarely encounters the plant today outside of a few remote sites in nature preserves.

Dwarf Ginseng

To give but a single common name for nearly any plant is to indulge a geographic bias: colloquial names, like regional dialects and like the plant species themselves, formed a mosaic across the American landscape. The similarity of many forest plant species to those known in Europe resulted in a host of vicarious names. Often the resemblance was only superficial, and misnomers were common.

Many plant names, such as "puccoon" for any plant that yielded dye, were adopted from the tribal languages of the American Indians, and, like similar names for rivers and landforms, were first bent into French, then twice Anglicized, by British, and finally American voices. Faster than the informed expeditions of European-educated scientists, who carefully assigned Linnaean epithets or fashioned new ones, the folk wisdom and language of the frontier was filling the wilderness with names. Red Puccoon, Corn Root, Red Indian Paint, Turmeric, Tetterwort, Pauson and Sweet Slumber are but some of the names given to the plant which most of us today know as Bloodroot (page 17).

Goldenseal

Hydrastis canadensis / RANUNCULACEAE

The rhizome of this plant exudes a bright yellowish-orange sap, prompting its other common names, Yellow Puccoon and Orange-root. Used both as a dye and a medicine, the wild species was all but exterminated in many parts of its range. While still an infrequent plant, in recent years it has literally gained ground as fewer human root-diggers are in the woods today. The alkaloid hydrastine does have known medicinal value, and there is still a market for both wild and cultivated harvests. There is also a sustained market for Ginseng and May-apple, however, continued sale of these is not based on any yet proven medicinal value.

Goldenseal

The strong odor characteristic of many plants is in some cases apparent to us only upon bruising particular plant tissues. Such damage releases enzymes which then activate the aromatic compounds. Mints are a good example. The final expense of energy is not made until the plant is actually mechanically threatened—clearly a conservation of energy phenomenon. From catnip to the most potent hallucinogenic plants, the subtle toxic chemistry of survival has shaped complex behaviors of avoidance or attraction, to a spectrum of animals from insects to man. They are but one example of the immense complexity of interaction which determines ecosystems.

False Rue-anemone

Isopyrum biternatum / RANUNCULACEAE

Its cluster of yellow stamens a typical buttercup flower, this fragile plant differs from the similar Rue-anemone (*Anemonella thalictroides*) by having leaves distinctly lobed (*bi-ternate*) rather than simply notched. Seen here beneath a branch of Witch-hazel (page 92), *Isopyrum* is common in moist woods. It persists in cut-over and grazed forests, parks and lawns, especially on calcareous soil. "Rue" is in common usage for several American wild flowers whose leaves resemble those of the sour-tasting European herb *Ruta graveolens*, of the Rutaceae. In Medieval times, this very bitter herb was eaten in a symbolic act of repentance, the "herb of grace," and was the *Ave-grace* of exorcism, hence its relation to sorrow and regret.

False Rue-anemone

Life is a windfall from a dying star. The sun's energy comes to us through the metabolism of green plants. Ecologically, plant and animal species are part of a larger whole, a system which in itself is an ultimate unit of survival, for it maintains the continuous flow of energy and nutrients necessary for life.

In this ecosystem, plants capture the energy of sunlight; organisms of decay reduce dead plant material, releasing nutrients for re-use. Over several hundred million years, animals have further elaborated the flow of energy, building complex food chains of herbivores and carnivores—all based initially on plant energy. Their bodies, too, decay, completing life cycles.

Even casual study of an ecosystem reveals an abiding truth— that the relationships between things are as important as the things themselves. Living things have meaning in terms of what they do. Life does not know the dancer from the dance.

Smooth Yellow Violet
Viola eriocarpa VIOLACEAE

The most common of the yellow violets, this species is found in moist woods and flood plains. It is seen here with leaves of Arrow-wood (*Viburnum dentatum*) against the trunk of Red Elm (*Ulmus rubra*). The Smooth Yellow Violet is more frequent in the northern half of the eastern deciduous forest, but is also common to the southern mountains. Violets are referred to by the ancients as sources of medicine and food. The Greek scholar Pythagoras considered violets as spinach and they have been widely used as pot herbs for centuries. Rich in vitamins A and C, they were often brewed as a tea and are still sugared and used as candy "messages of love" in Appalachia.

Smooth Yellow Violet

A forest ecosystem is a sum of strategies. It is this sum and the diversity it represents which make a forest resilient to change. The diversity is revealed in the life histories of various species. Here differences and similarities are apparent. All plants overlap in what they do, yet their specific niches, their precise roles in the ecosystem, vary.

Tree species, as well as herbs and shrubs, are chiefly adapted to either early or late stages of forest development or succession. The late stage climax species like beech and maple preside in dominance over old-growth, mature forest systems. Early-stage pioneer, or invader, species are quick to occupy any forest site opened by wind or fire or the work of man.

Blue Phlox
Phlox divaricata / POLEMONIACEAE

Variable blue to purple or white flowers of diverse size are typical of this familiar species. Recognized forms include *albiflora*, a white-flowered variant, and the small-lobed corolla form, *Coulteri*, named for John Merle Coulter who described it in western Indiana. The plant is often called Sweet William, a name more accurately applied to the cultivated *Dianthus barbatus* of the Pink family. Blue Phlox is seen here sharing the light of a mesic forest floor with seedlings of Sugar Maple.

Blue Phlox

Sassafras, wild cherry and tulip tree (yellow poplar) are found growing in forests with beech and maple, but they differ from these in the amount of light required for producing sugar by photosynthesis. The climax species require comparatively low light intensity and grow up in the shade of other trees. The pioneer species, with seeds readily dispersed by wind or in edible fruits taken by birds, germinate and prosper in open sunlight and so are able to colonize wind-throws, burns, or abandoned fields.

Early settlers found such colonies of tulip tree commonly in groves of even-aged trees, straight and tall, with trunks nearly free of limbs. The wood proved soft and worked easily with an axe, yet it weathered well and resisted decay. This durability along with the growth habit of the species made it the most coveted tree for log cabin timbers.

White Baneberry
Actaea alba / RANUNCULACEAE

The beautiful, delicate flower clusters of Baneberry are scattered here with Wild Geranium (page 91) on a moist forest slope in late May. The common name alludes to the poisonous fruit of the European *A. spirata*, which indeed has caused severe illness and death in children. Our American species are less potent but are respected as powerful purgatives and emetics. Fruits mature to white berries with conspicuous dark spots where the stigma was attached, inspiring another common name, Doll's-eyes. The similar and slightly more northern-ranging species, Red Baneberry, *A. rubra,* differs primarily in the red color of the fruit, which is borne on thinner pedicels.

White Baneberry

From the ecosystem's standpoint, the vitality of pioneer species assures a long-term resiliency, by permitting natural "repair" of local damage. The temperate deciduous forest is very durable, compared to forests of the tropical or boreal zones. It has a well-developed reserve of nutrients and energy which is readily available. Mature forests have two types of food chains. A familiar one, the grazing food chain, builds from green leaves. The detritus food chain starts with energy accumulated in dead leaves and twigs, building from the litter of the forest floor. The litter, humus and organic-rich topsoil contain seeds and nutrients which, upon destruction of the forest cover, can begin a regrowth.

Bishop's-cap

Mitella diphylla / SAXIFRAGACEAE

In a mosaic here with common associates, Maidenhair Fern (*Adiantum pedatum*) and Toothwort (page 25), *Mitella*'s wisps of white bloom are unobtrusive. Magnified, the flowers reveal a complex and lacey symmetry. Delicate petals pinnately cleft explain this common name and its other, Miterwort, a miter or mitre being the tall pointed hat with peaks in front and back, worn by various ecclesiastics. The plant is common to infrequent through rich woods of the eastern deciduous forest.

Bishop's-cap

In the moist tropics, temperatures are high and growth seasons long or continuous, so litter decays rapidly. Unabsorbed nutrients are quickly leached away. In the boreal forest, growth seasons are brief, temperatures low, and the acid litter inhibits decay bacteria, slowing the release of nutrients. In both systems the resilience to damage is much less than in the deciduous forests of the temperate zone because nutrient pools are small and the soils vulnerable to catastrophic erosion. The resiliency of a forest comes from the ease by which damage is repaired.

Allegheny Foamflower
Tiarella cordifolia / SAXIFRAGACEAE

The name of this plant, like the preceding, also translates to headgear, as "little tiara." Its foam-like inflorescence is also similar; the plant is somewhat larger, its leaves smoother and more coarsely toothed. The leaf shape bears a resemblance to the romantic rendition of the human heart, hence the species name, *cordifolia*. A western member of the original Tertiary flora, the genus includes other species from Japan to the Himalayas. While the common name implies its prevalence and first discovery in our eastern mountains, this species ranges west to the prairie in Indiana, then north to Minnesota.

Allegheny Foamflower

The temperate zone, however, is anything but temperate, as those who live there have experienced. Temperatures fluctuate between lows as cold as the arctic and highs as hot as the tropics. Temperatures may change sixty degrees in a matter of hours. This presents incredible problems for stationary life forms such as plants. Temperate zone floras exhibit various modes of winter hardiness. In their evolution, deciduous species first became adapted to drought.

Winter creates a physiological drought, for water is periodically frozen and unavailable. The damage wrought by winter is rarely from the cold. At low temperatures, plant tissues convert starch to sugar, producing more molecules as a kind of antifreeze. Southern species, at their northern range, are generally found on north-facing slopes, away from winter sunlight. Sunlight warms a plant, begins to dry it out during a time when water is frozen in the ground. Warm days can simply desiccate or "sun-scald" the plants.

Wild Columbine
Aquilegia canadensis / RANUNCULACEAE

From April to July these ornately beautiful flowers may be seen in a wide range of color forms and in habitats from dry woods and hillsides to wet valleys and even peat bogs. The genus is classic in pollination ecology: flower color segregates pollinators, thus maintaining genetic separateness of populations. Five divisions of the genus, perfectly inter-fertile, may grow intermixed yet remain genetically discrete. Hybridization occurs sporadically due to non-discriminant bumble bees, and species within each division are known to merge. The genus name is attributed by some authors to be from the Latin for eagle (*aquila*), presumably in reference to the flower's spurs as talons. Others claim it is from *aqua*, water, and *legere*, to collect. The man who knew has evidently been lost in antiquity.

Wild Columbine

A warm day in midwinter presents a problem of environmental cue: how does a species know that it is not spring? Why are plants not fooled? Some are, but rarely the true north temperate plants. Adaptation involves both a cue of day-length and a summing of hours above some particular threshold of temperature. As days become longer and warmer, a series of metabolic events must occur which require a long, progressive initiation. This length of time required is the hedge against false beginnings. Plants which lack such internal "wisdom" for reading environmental cues simply do not survive.

The patterns of fruit evolution reveal a bettering of mechanisms for dispersal. Ovary wall is found elaborated into wings, barbs, hooks or to fleshy fruit tissue, edible but with digestion-resistant seedcoats. All reflect the evolutionary value of strategic modes of mobility for the plant species involved.

Solomon's-seal

Polygonatum biflorum / LILIACEAE

A delicate arch in the shade of a forest in late May, the "many jointed" (*poly-gonatum*) stem has alternate leaves bearing one to four axillary flowers (often two, hence *bi-florum*). Its common name is said to refer to the circular "seal-like" scar left on the rhizomatous root by the dead flowering stalk. Fertile flowers mature into dark blue berries. The root stalks are edible, and the young leafy shoots have been boiled and eaten like asparagus.

Solomon's-seal

Adaptation, as we have seen in pollination, frequently involves species interaction. Beyond the intricacies of floral anatomy, a host of adaptations comprise any plant's fitness to its environment. One of the most ubiquitous of these is the symbiotic association between certain fungi and the roots of flowering plants. These mycorrhizae afford many benefits. The fungus benefits by having a sugar supply from the green plant. In return, it absorbs and transmits nutrients, especially nitrogen. In soils which are nutrient-poor, this nutrient scavenging role of the symbiotic fungus is crucial to the higher plant's survival. Most forest trees and many herbs are dependent on mycorrhizal fungi, and their ecological range is in part determined by soil conditions hospitable to the fungus. Most fungi prefer relatively acid soils. Grassland soils are frequently neutral or even alkaline, and species range maps indicate great numbers of forest species whose ranges halt abruptly along the prairie border where the change in soil conditions is equally abrupt.

Moccasin Flower
Cypripedium acaule / ORCHIDACEAE

Seen here with a seedling of Chestnut Oak (*Quercus prinus*) rooted in oak and pine litter, this increasingly rare orchid is restricted to acidic settings, either wet or dry. As with many other plants, and orchids in particular, site requirements relate more precisely to the essential symbiotic fungi of the plant's roots. These mycorrhizae, which aid the plant in nutrient uptake, require an acidic organic substrate. The plant's genus name refers to Aphrodite of Cyprus (becoming in Latin *cypri-*), and *pedium* for her slipper. The general resemblance of the flower to a slipper or shoe is remarked also in the Indian allusion of the common name.

Moccasin Flower

Flowering itself is initiated by environmental cue, hormone levels which, in turn, are regulated by a light-sensitive pigment, phytochrome, changing its form between day and night. The pigment is reversible, one phase building in daylight, the other accumulating during the night. This accumulation or decline of a substance which regulates flowering allows a plant to "recognize" the progression of season with length of day being the cue. Plants of the midsummer forest come into bloom as days grow longer. They nod above the withered flowers which formed the quilt of April. Daylength is the one constant by which all life can set its clock, timing the critical life cycle stages.

Yellow Lady's-slipper
Cypripedium Calceolus / ORCHIDACEAE

Orchids are among the most intricately evolved plants on earth. With highly advanced adaptation to their pollinators, the family has inspired almost a special science of orchid pollination, and probably no other non-crop plant group has been so extensively studied or written about. In his later research career, Charles Darwin became fascinated with the pollination ecology of orchids and made many significant observations. Pollination in *Cypripedium* seems to be by deceit, using odor with no food offering. The insect is simply trapped in the "slipper." As in other orchids, strong visual signals may also be involved. In attempting to find an exit, the insect accomplishes pollination, since to escape, it must climb across the stigma. A barrier to self-pollination is achieved by the different maturation times of male and female structures, the pistil maturing first. Two varieties of this species are recognized, this one being var. *parviflorum*. Among diagnostic traits are the smaller size and brownish purple color of the lateral petals.

Yellow Lady's-slipper

The perfecting of dormancy became the crucial adaptation of deciduous plants. The onset of dormancy, like its interruption, is cued by light, in the length of the days.

As daylength wanes, plant hormone levels drop and their high concentration no longer inhibits the growth of abscission tissue, at the base of each leaf. A corky leaf scar forms, the petiole is slowly dammed up, and the leaf is slowly cut off from water.

As temperatures drop, a plant burns less sugar than it makes during the sunlit hours and excess sugars accumulate. The red pigment in plants, anthocyanin, is a molecule made of sugar. Leaves red with this pigment reflect more heat and lose less water. Many winter buds are red with anthocyanin, protecting the embryonic bud from desiccation in winter sunlight. In many autumn leaves, such as those of sugar maple, there is, in effect, the same attempt. Water is depleted as the leaf is walled off from the stem. Chlorophyll fades and the yellow pigments in the leaf become apparent. If there is enough trapped sugar, the yellow leaves flag scarlet.

Goat's-beard

Aruncus dioicus / ROSACEAE

This tall herbaceous member of the Rose family lacks the stipules characteristic of its family, and is dioecious, having separate male and female plants. *Aruncus* is one of several plants bearing superficial resemblance to Ginseng, and it has undoubtedly been mistaken by novice "sang" hunters. A wide-ranging plant, it thrives primarily on mesic slopes and shady cliffs. In the southern Appalachians it is common even along roadsides.

Goat's-beard

By October, the forest is burning amber and crimson in the brief evening light. There is a sharp and pungent sweetness to the air— the smell of walnuts. The nights are cold.

A sudden wind drifts storms of yellow leaves and tumbles fruits and seeds. A night rain breaks the last dead leaves away from ash and maple. The walnut trees are long since bare—the last to get their leaves, the first to lose them. Here and there in the dry oak woods, a clatter of acorns breaks the stillness. The youngest oak and beech trees wear their dead, russet foliage into winter. The wild flowers are only a rumor now. The plants are dormant. All the ancient strategies are one.

Wild Geranium

Geranium maculatum / GERANIACEAE

This species flowers in profusion from April to late July. Here it shares the deep shade of the summer-green forest with ferns (*Polypodium virginianum* and *Dryopteris marginalis*). Plants of this widespread genus are often called Cranes-bills and indeed the name is from the Greek *geranos* for the long-billed birds we call cranes. (The long, curled style of the ovary, which persists on the fruit, is the imagined bill.) The familiar cultivated Geranium, *Pelargonium hortorum*, belongs to a different genus of the family. Precisely timed flower maturation in Geranium prolongs pollen availability and avoids self-pollination. Stamens of a single flower mature sequentially and, like the other flower parts, absciss one at a time. Only when the last anther has ripened and fallen does the pistil emerge receptive. "They die and fall whose errand is complete."

Wild Geranium

Epilogue

In preserving the forest habitats of these wild flowers as living museums it is clear, too, that we save a refuge of human thought and feeling. To the first generations of Americans, centuries ago, the deciduous forest was home. And forever embedded in a nation's memory is a clearing of light—stumpland circling a cabin and beyond the fence rails a walking distance—all the world we knew, winter and summer. Those who watched the strange and many barks, mile upon mile, grow dark in evening snow, perhaps drew a vaster meaning out of April, having foregone family, friends and comfort for a lonely land where youth was brief. So far away in time, can we wholly comprehend such gift of flowers? Carpet of Trout-lily and Violets to cover tiny graves; Spring-beauty and Trillium—these were our heritage.
Have we come so far?

Witch-hazel
Hamamelis virginiana / HAMAMELIDACEAE

This common species of Witch-hazel is one of three in North America. Its family is old, with most members found closer to the center of origin of flowering plants, in Southeastern Asia. Well-known to the Indians and pioneers of the New World, its leaves and twigs were retted in water or alcohol (tinctures) for a fragrant liniment. Found from Canada to Florida and west to Texas, it was cut by frontiersmen and later by both Union and Confederate soldiers as camouflage, for it wilts very slowly. So befitting the tenacity of a people who found and used it, the plant flowers in late fall amid its own dying leaves, then matures its fruits into a second autumn.

Witch-hazel

Suggestions for Further Reading

Anderson, Edgar. 1952. *Plants, Man and Life*. Little, Brown and Company, Boston.

Braun, E. Lucy. 1950. *Deciduous Forests of Eastern North America*. The Blakiston Company, Toronto.

Cain, Stanley A. 1971. *Foundations of Plant Geography*. Hafner Publishing Company, New York.

Cronquist, Arthur. 1968. *The Evolution and Classification of Flowering Plants*. Houghton Mifflin Company, Boston.

Eifert, Virginia S. 1965. *Tall Trees and Far Horizons*. Dodd, Mead and Company, New York.

Faegri, K., and L. van der Pijl. 1966. *The Principles of Pollination Ecology*. Pergamon Press, Toronto.

Fernald, Merrit Lyndon, and Alfred Charles Kinsey, revised by Reed C. Rollins. 1958. *Edible Wild Plants of Eastern North America*. Harper & Row, New York.

Gleason, Henry A., and Arthur Cronquist. 1963. *Manual of Vascular Plants of Northeastern United States and Adjacent Canada*. D. Van Nostrand Company, Inc., Princeton, N. J.

Grieve, M. 1959. *A Modern Herbal*, Volumes I and II. Hafner Publishing Company, New York.

Holt, Perry C., and Robert A. Paterson. 1970. *The Distributional History of the Biota of the Southern Appalachians*. Part II—Flora. Virginia Polytechnic Institute and State University, Blacksburg, Virginia.

Kingsbury, John M. 1964. *Poisonous Plants of the United States and Canada*. Prentice-Hall, Inc., Englewood Cliffs, N. J.

Lillard, Richard G. 1947. *The Great Forest*. Alfred A. Knopf, New York.

McCormick, Jack. 1966. *The Life of the Forest*. McGraw-Hill Book Company, New York.

Percival, Mary S. 1965. *Floral Biology*. Pergamon Press, Ltd., London.

Platt, Rutherford. 1947. *Our Flowering World*. Dodd, Mead and Company, New York.

Rickett, Harold William. 1966. *Wild Flowers of the United States: The Northeastern States*, Volumes I and II. McGraw-Hill Book Company, New York.

Takhtajan, Armen. 1969. *Flowering Plants, Origin and Dispersal*. Smithsonian Institution Press, Washington, D.C.

Thomas, William L., ed. 1956. *Man's Role in Changing the Face of the Earth*. University of Chicago Press, Chicago.

Wharton, Mary E., and Roger W. Barbour. 1971. *A Guide to the Wildflowers and Ferns of Kentucky*. The University Press of Kentucky, Lexington, Kentucky.

Index to Plants Pictured

Nomenclature according to Gleason and Cronquist, 1963; family names updated.

Designed by Michael Stancik, Jr.
Color separations by Jeremiah Hill,
American Litho Arts, Lombard, Ill.
General printing Contractor and
supervision
SEIDEL, FARRIS, CLARK INCORPORATED
Toledo, Ohio, 43696